peaceful piano pla

A collection of 35 beautiful piano solos

I Giorni

Composed by Ludovico Einaudi

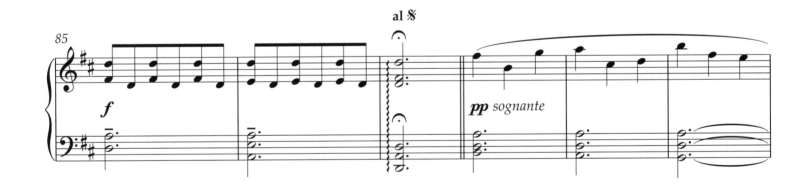

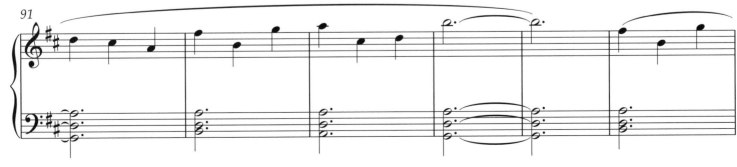

6

allarg.

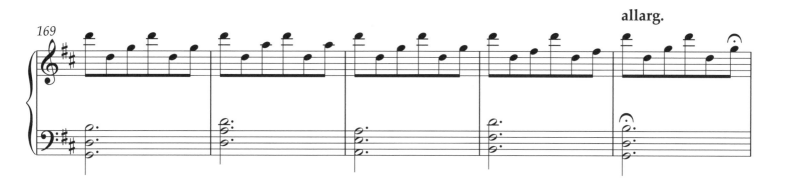

a tempo

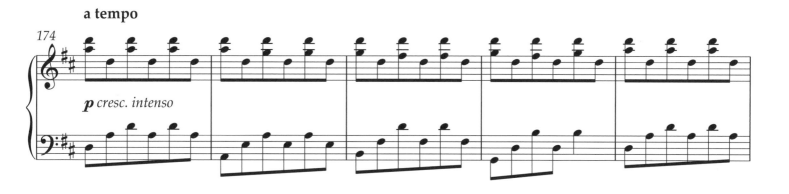

accel. _ _ _ _ _ _ _ _ _ _ molto

Ab Ovo

Composed by Joep Beving

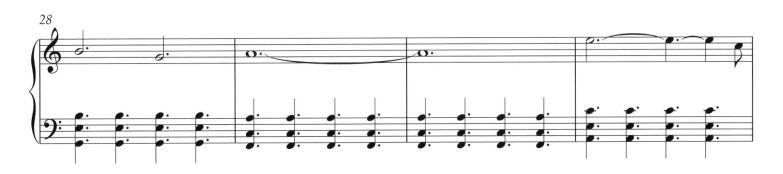

Written On The Sky

Composed by Max Richter

15

Gymnopédie No. 3
'Lent e grave in A minor'

Composed by Erik Satie

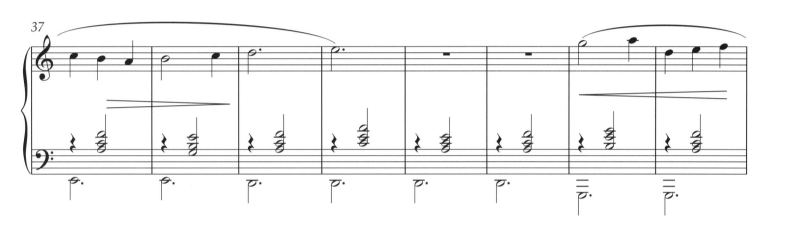

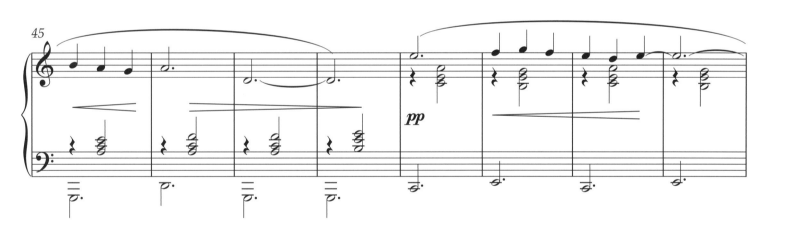

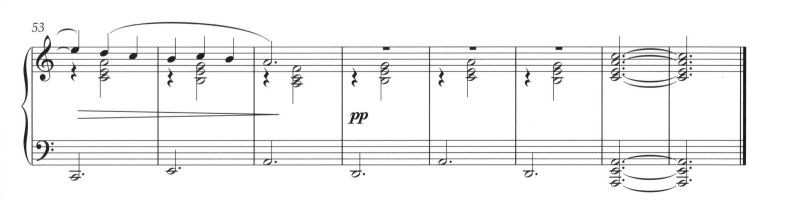

Mass (Re-Imagined)

Composed by Phoria

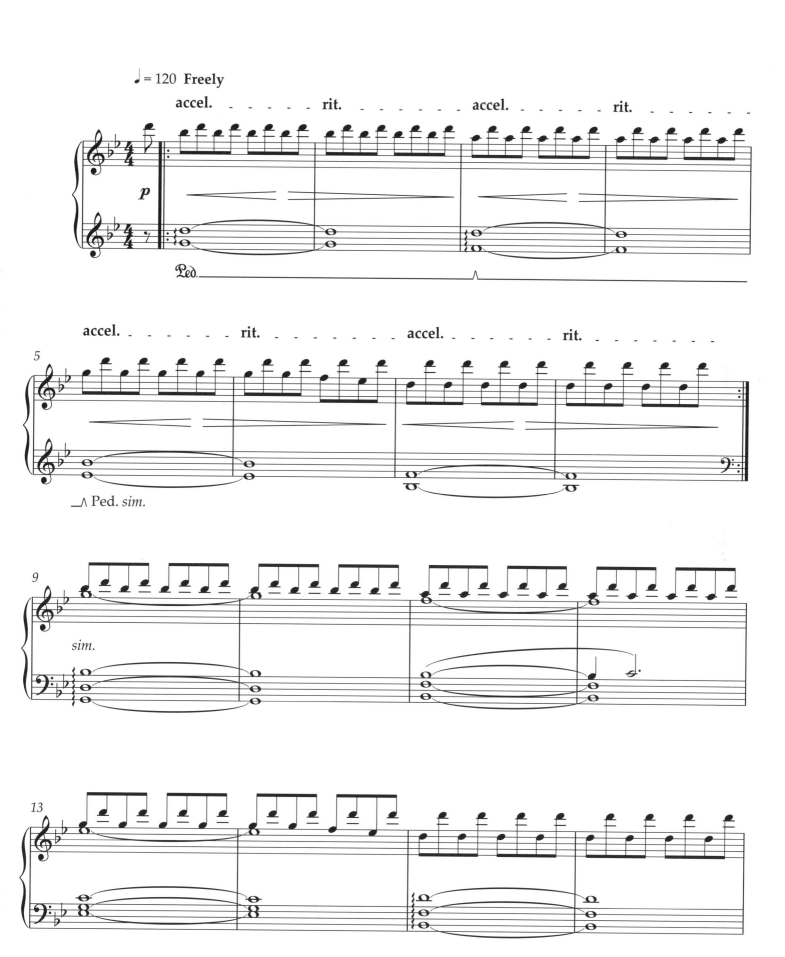

21

Pathétique Sonata
Op. 13 No. 8 (second movement)

Composed by Ludwig van Beethoven

Earnestly Yours

Composed by Keaton Henson

The Tearjerker Returns

Composed by Jarvis Cocker, Jason Beck and Ryuichi Sakamoto

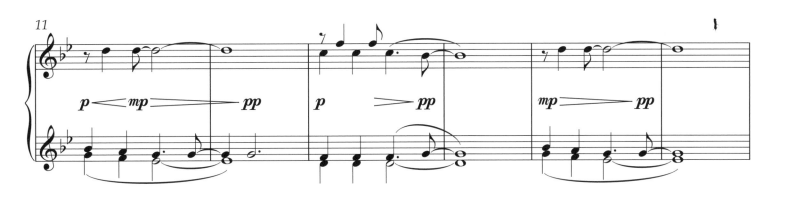

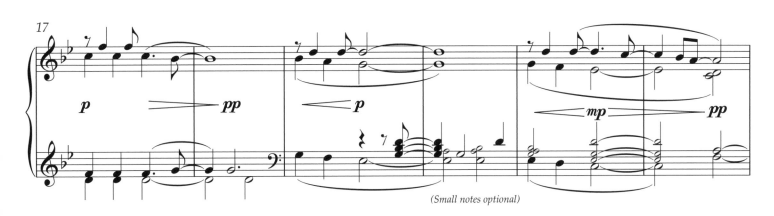

(Small notes optional)

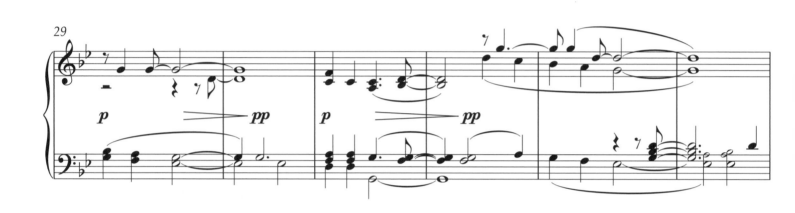

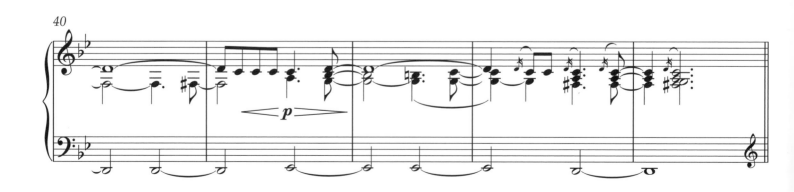

Chord Left

Composed by Agnes Obel

(Omit small notes if necessary)

rit. - - - - - - - -

Engagement Party

Composed by Justin Hurwitz

Pedal ad lib. throughout

Last Song

Composed by Alexis Ffrench

Clair de Lune

Composed by Claude Debussy

Andante très expressif

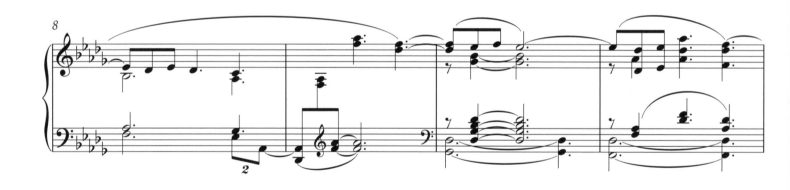

Throes

Composed by Isaac Symonds, Dylan Phillips, Conner Mollander and Devon Portielje

Aria
(from 'Goldberg Variations, BWV 988')

Composed by Johann Sebastian Bach

♩ = 76

Merry Christmas Mr Lawrence

Composed by Ryuichi Sakamoto

without Ped.

with Ped.

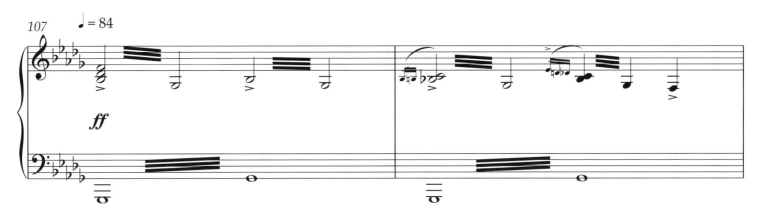

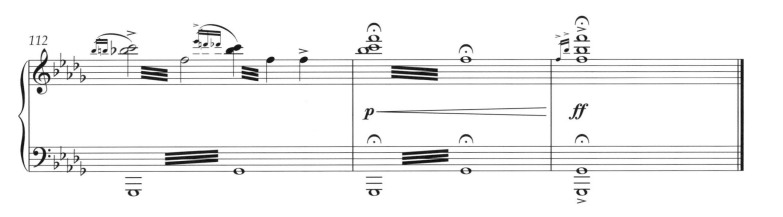

What We Are

Composed by Anne Lovett

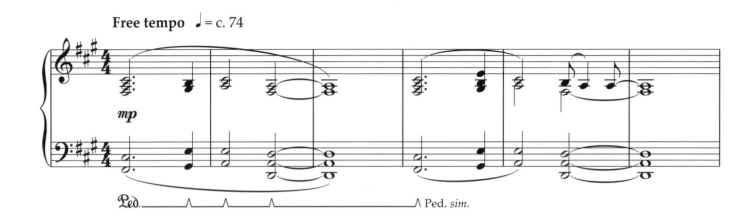

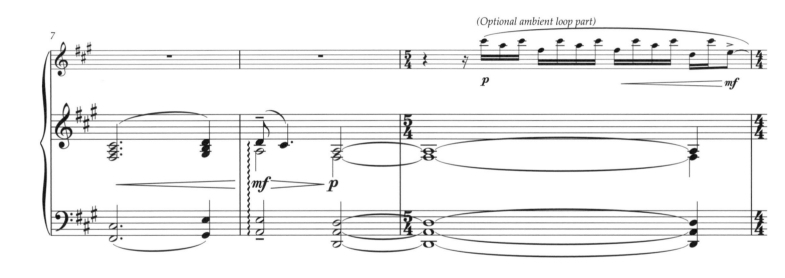

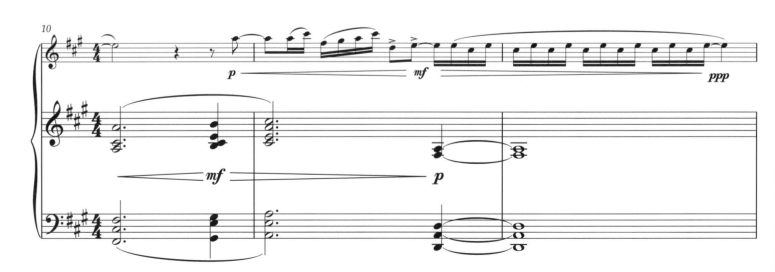

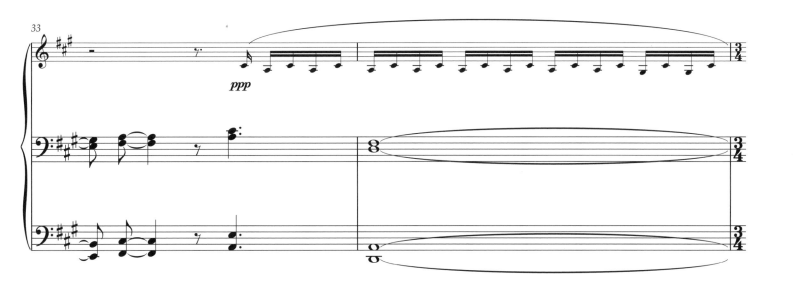

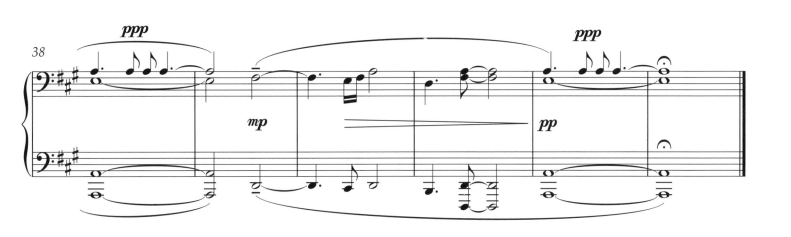

Adagio in G minor

Composed by Tomaso Albinoni

Faith's Song
(from 'Keeping Faith')

Composed by Laurence Love Greed

Flora

Composed by Henrik Lindstrand

Pavane pour une Infante défunte

Composed by Maurice Ravel

Prelude in C
(BWV846 from 'The Well-Tempered Clavier Book 1')

Composed by Johann Sebastian Bach

Allegro ♩ = 112

Inizio

Composed by Ludovico Einaudi

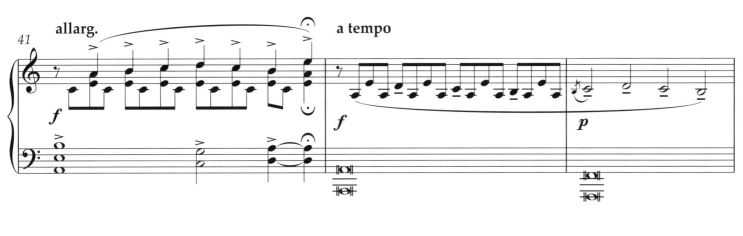

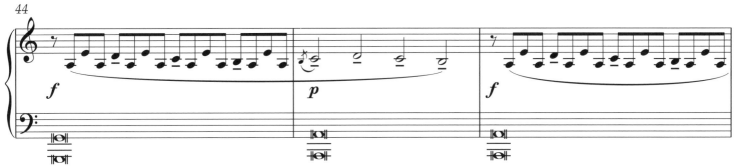

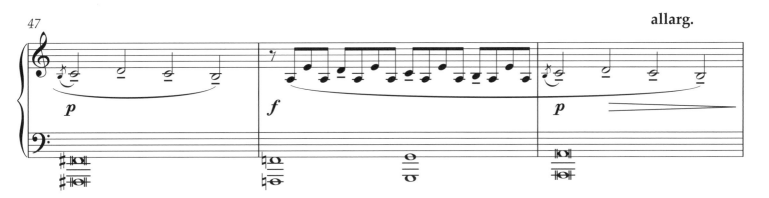

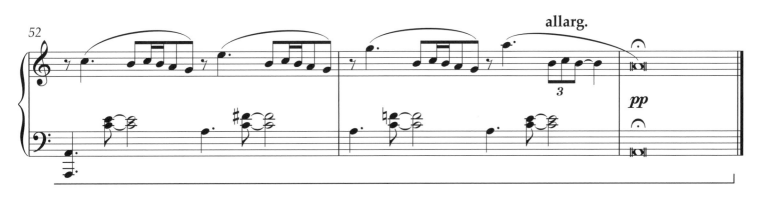

Strata

Composed by Poppy Ackroyd

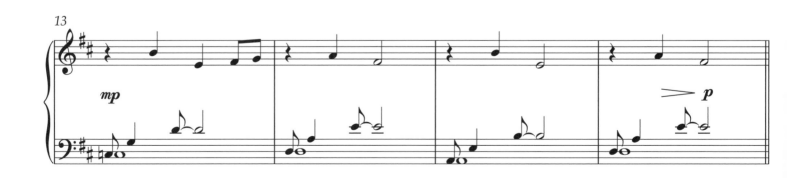

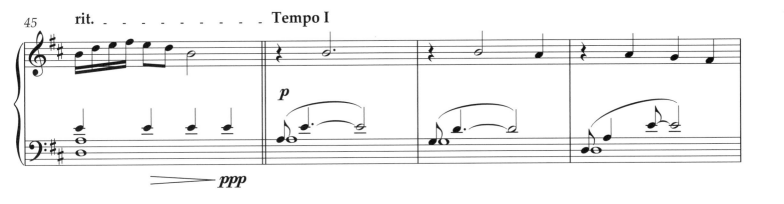

Piano Piece, Imperfect Moments Pt. 4

Composed by Johannes Brecht

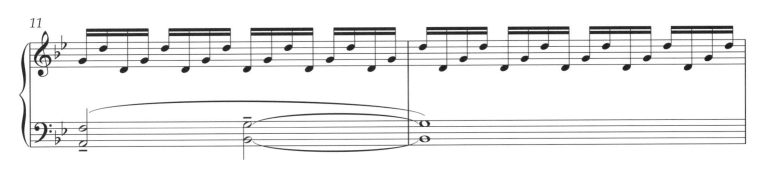

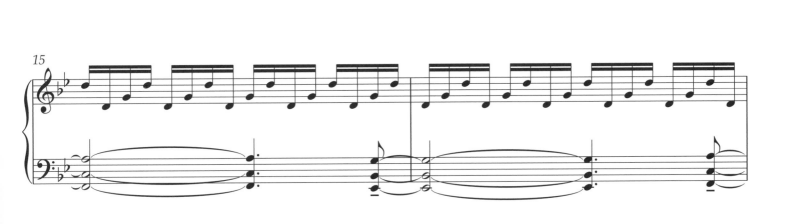

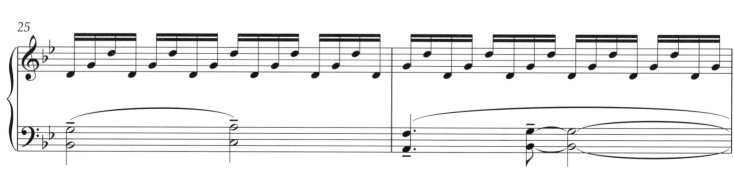

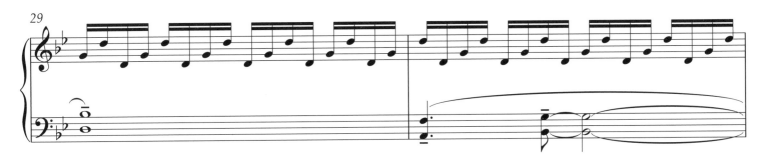

poco a poco

mp cresc. poco a poco

mf cresc. poco a poco

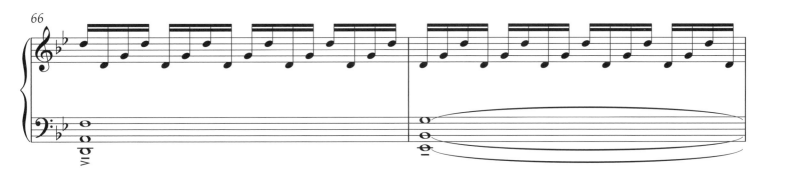

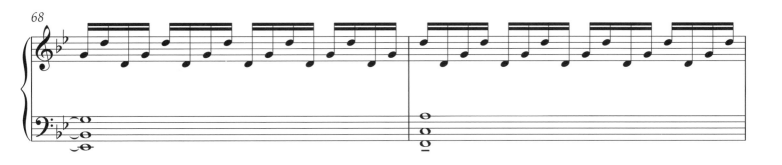

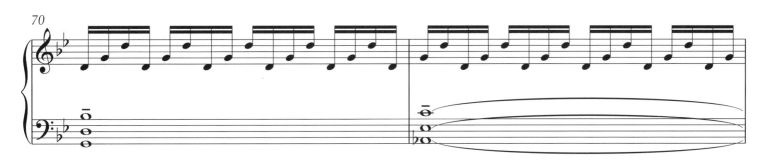

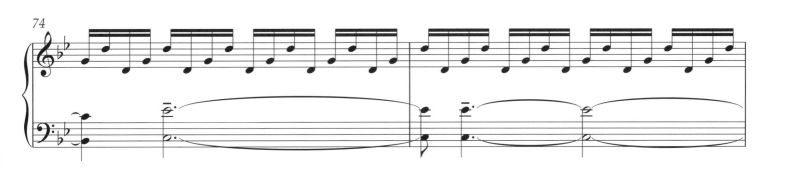

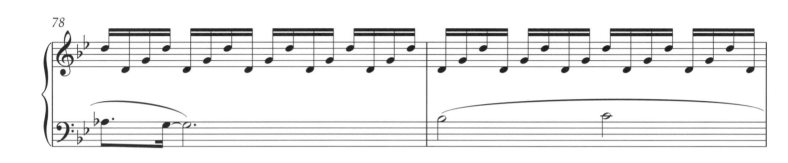

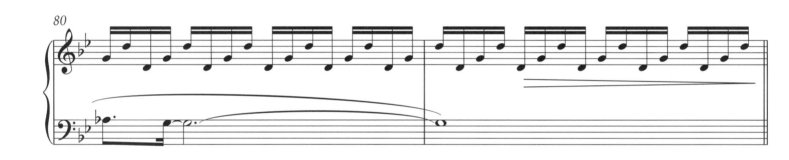

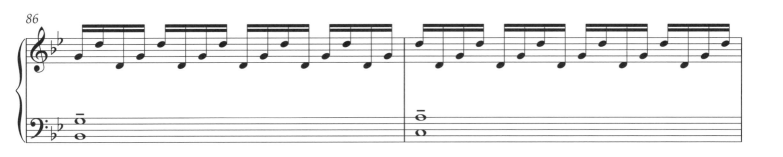

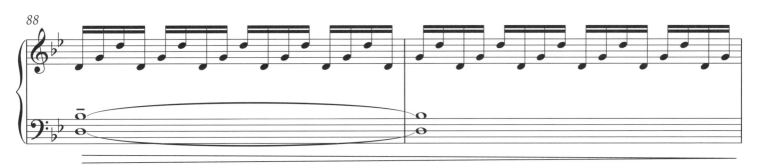

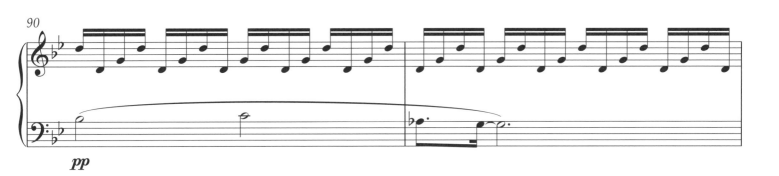

To The Order Of Night

Composed by Robert Lowe

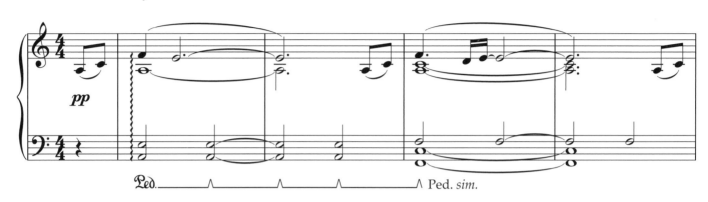

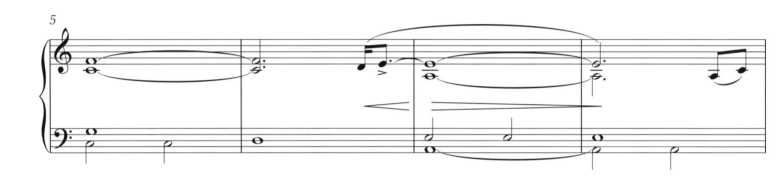

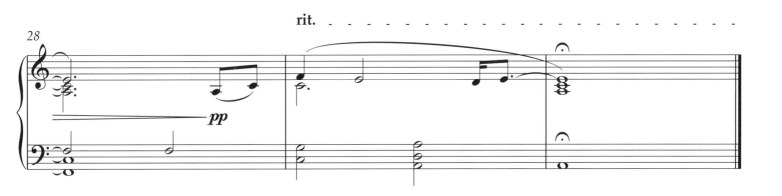

Mandus

Composed by Jessica Curry

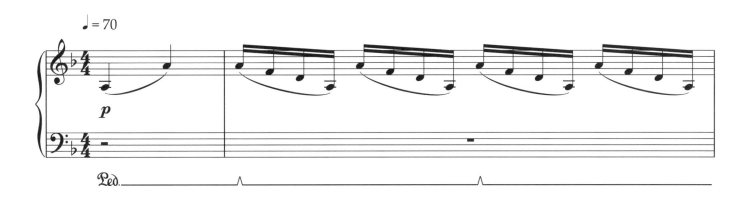

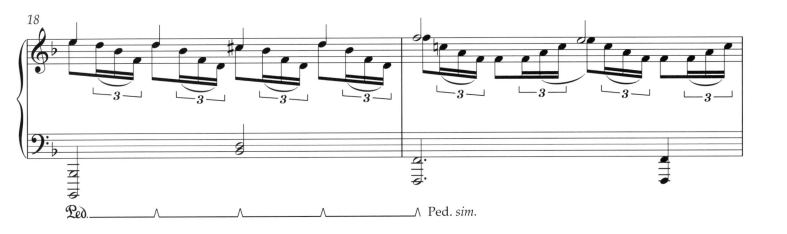

Prelude in B minor
(Op.28 No.6)

Composed by Frederic Chopin

Lento assai

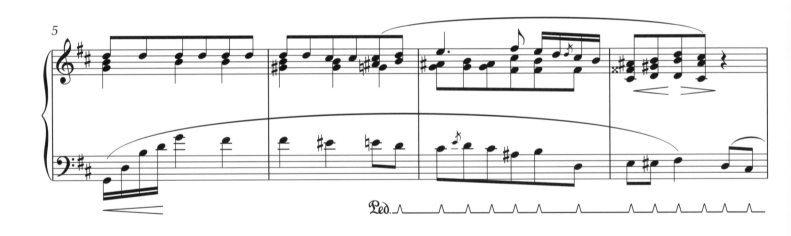

The Departure
(from 'The Leftovers')

Composed by Max Richter

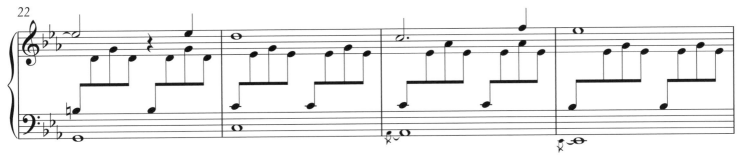

Petrichor

Composed by Keaton Henson

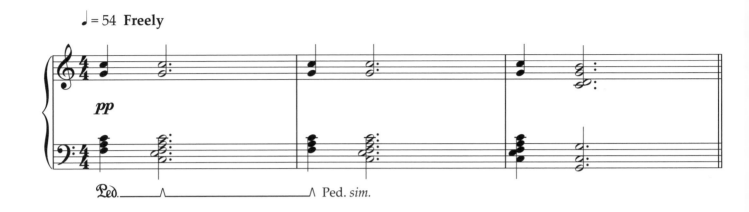

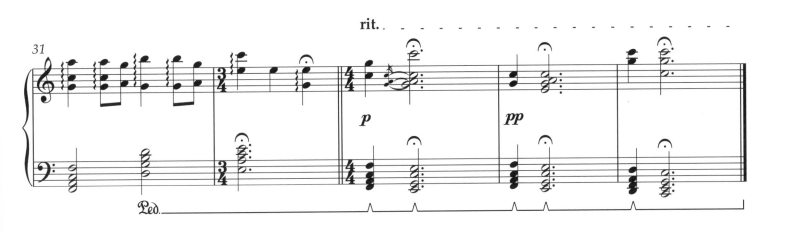

New Moon

Composed by Alexandre Desplat

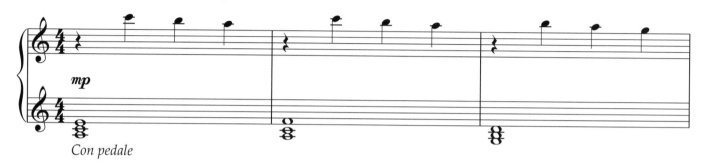

Adagio
(from Piano Sonata No. 12 in F, K332)

Composed by Wolfgang Amadeus Mozart

Träumerei
(from Kinderszenen Op.15)

Composed by Robert Schumann

Variations on the Kanon

Composed by Johann Pachelbel
Arranged by George Winston

Moderate tempo

Meeting Points At 2AM

Composed by Ondřej Holý

Clouds

Composed by Pam Wedgwood

Cover Image: Black piano, 2004 (acrylic on paper),
Seligman, Lincoln /Private Collection / Bridgeman Images

Designed by Kenosha
New transcriptions by Oliver Weeks
Edited by Lucy Holliday & Rebecca Castell

© 2019 by Faber Music Ltd
First published by Faber Music Ltd in 2019
Bloomsbury House
74–77 Great Russell Street
London WC1B 3DA

Printed in England by Caligraving Ltd
All rights reserved

ISBN: 0-571-54103-8
EAN: 978-0-571-54103-4

To buy Faber Music publications or to find out about the full range of titles available,
please contact your local music retailer or Faber Music sales enquiries:

Faber Music Limited, Burnt Mill, Elizabeth Way, Harlow CM20 2HX
Tel: +44 (0)1279 82 89 82   Fax: +44 (0)1279 82 89 83
sales@fabermusic.com   fabermusicstore.com